Fien & Teun

and the mighty mills of Unesco Kinderdijk

Cock-a-doodle-doo! Randy the rooster crows. Teun wakes up, jumps out of bed and opens the curtains. It's snowing! Quickly he wakes up Fien, 'Fien! Fien! It's snowing!' Fien rubs her eyes. Teun is right. It's snowing! 'Come on, Teun. Let's see if mommy and daddy are up already.'

'It's snowing, it's snowing!', Teun shouts while cheerfully jumping around the room. Mom laughs, 'Yes, Teun, it's snowing.' 'Could we go outside and play in the snow?', Fien asks. 'Sure you can', dad says. 'But you will have to wear your clogs. Or else your socks get wet.' 'Okay', Fien and Teun shout together.

Teun steps outside. The snow squeaks under his feet. 'Look, Fien. It looks like the farm is covered in powdered sugar.' Fien laughs. Suddenly she makes a funny sound, 'Whaaa!' 'What is it, Fien?' 'A big cold drop of water fell on my neck.' Teun looks at Fien with surprise, 'How is that possible? It's not even raining.' 'No, it's not raining. I don't know.' Dad walks through the door, 'Would you two like to go sledding?' Fien and Teun jump up, 'Yes, let's go!'

When they sit on the sled, Fien asks, 'Daddy? How is it possible that a cold drop of water fell on my neck?' Dad smiles, 'I think the snow is melting.' 'Melting?' What's that?', Teun asks. 'You know that it only snows when it's cold outside, right?' Fien en Teun nod. 'Snow is water which became really cold. That's called freezing. When the weather gets warmer again, snow turns into cold water. That's called melting. And this melted cold water is what fell on your neck!' Fien laughs, 'But where does all the melted water go?' 'I will show you. Come on.'

Dad points to the other side, 'Look, there is Kinderdijk. Just like our farm Kinderdijk lies in the polder. Polders lie very low. When the snow melts or if it rains very hard, the ditches in the polders will be filled with water. Just like a bath tub with water. Sometimes there is so much water in the ditches that they overflow and the water from the ditches runs to the farms. That's why, a long time ago, people built mills in Kinderdijk. These mills make sure the water can flow out of the ditches so we don't get wet feet.' 'But, how do they do that?', Teun asks. Dad smiles, 'Miller Björn can tell you all about it. Let's see if he's home.'

After some time on the sled they see miller Björn outside waving at them. 'Hello, Fien. Hello, Teun. How wonderful to see you!' Fien shakes the miller's hand, 'Hello, sir. Daddy says this mill makes sure our feet don't get wet. How's that possible?' The miller points at the mill, 'Look. Next to the mill is a big wheel. That's a scoop wheel. When the wind blows, the sails of the mill will start to turn and then the scoop wheel also starts to turn. The wheel scoops up the water. Just like someone empties the bath tub with a bucket.' Teun looks at the miller with surprise, 'But, where does all that water go?'

'Look,' the miller says, 'in Kinderdijk there are a lot of these mills. All these mills together make sure the water gets scooped up. The mills scoop the water from the polders to the river. And the river takes the water back to sea. This way the water doesn't bother us anymore in Kinderdijk and our feet stay dry.' 'How clever', Fien says. 'Very clever', miller Björn answers.

'Can I make the mill spin?', Teun asks. 'Of course you can!', the miller says. 'First we have to make sure the sails face the wind.' 'How do we do that?', Fien asks. 'By moving this big turning wheel. But you need to have big muscles.' Teun jumps up, 'Daddy says I'm the strongest farmer in the whole world.'

When the sails face the wind, Teun pulls the rope. The sails of the mill begin to turn. First slowly, then more quickly. The scoop wheel starts to work as well. Fien looks at the wheel, 'Teun, look at this. The water is coming up.' Quickly Teun runs to Fien. 'Watch out, don't get wet!', miller Björn shouts laughing.

Wide-eyed Fien and Teun look at the mill and the scoop wheel. 'We've done that all by ourselves! Right, Fien?', Teun says. 'Yes, Teun. And without your muscles we couldn't have done it.' Teun feels proud. Miller Björn shows up with a gift, 'Here you go, because you two helped me so well.' Fien looks at the gift, 'It's a small mill!' 'That's right! Now you can play at home on the farm in the melting snow, without getting your feet wet. And all because of your very own mill.'

When Fien and Teun return home, they quickly go to work. With a big brush Teun paints all the pieces of the mill. Fien takes a good look at the drawing and puts the mill together. Suddenly Teun sneezes. His brush slips and his face is covered in white paint. Fien giggles, 'You look like a snowman, Teun.' Teun laughs and puts his brush on Fien's nose: 'You too!' Fien smiles, 'Silly, naughty Teun.'

turning wheel

sails

mill

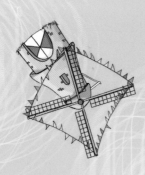

ditch